TAKE FLIGHT
Merrill Linguistic Reading Program

Fourth Edition

Based on the philosophy of Charles C. Fries

Authors:

Rosemary G. Wilson
Former Assistant Director of Reading,
English, and Language Arts
Philadelphia Public Schools
Philadelphia, Pennsylvania

Mildred K. Rudolph
Former District Language Arts Supervisor
Philadelphia Public Schools
Philadelphia, Pennsylvania

Consultants:

Timothy E. Heron
Ohio State University
Columbus, Ohio

Lois Michel Plous
Learning Disability Specialist
Milwaukee Public Schools
Milwaukee, Wisconsin

Charles E. Merrill Publishing Co.
Bell & Howell Company
London • Toronto • Sydney

TABLE OF CONTENTS

ISBN-0-675-01327-5

Published by
Charles E. Merrill Publishing Co.
A Bell & Howell Company
Columbus, Ohio 43216

might
sight
night
tight
flight
bright

people

because

bite	might	tight	sight
site	sight	night	flight
might	tight	flight	bright

Rockets

Mr. Kelly had a book called "A Rocket Flight to the Stars." When he told the class about this book, everyone wanted to read it. They liked the book so much they all became interested in rockets and wanted to read other books about them.

Mr. Kelly said, "As it happens, I have another rocket book you might like. This one tells how rocket flight began."

Jan said her mother had a book about rockets. "I think she might let us use it," said Jan. "I'll see if I can bring it on Monday."

That night Jan asked her mom about the book. "Yes, you may take it to school," said Mrs. Bell.

Jan went into her mom's room and turned on the light. The book she was looking for was bright red. She could see it, but she couldn't quite reach it because it was on the top shelf. So she set a little stepladder by the shelf. Then she stood on it to reach the book. The book was squeezed tightly between the other books on the shelf, but Jan got it with no problem. She sat by the light and began to read. "This will be perfect!" she said to herself. "Wow! What a sight—a mighty rocket blasting right into orbit with a flashing tail as bright as a flame!"

Jan began to think what fun it would be to blast off in a rocket. "I suppose in twenty years lots of people might be riding in rockets," she said to herself. She dreamed she could take off in orbit and just lean back in her chair as her rocket steered past the bright stars.

As she looked at the book, Jan began to see lots of things she wanted to tell her class. Rockets were probably invented hundreds of years ago by the Chinese. Those rockets were used for big displays of light in the night sky. Later, rockets were used in battles.

Rockets are very powerful. They can go much faster than jets. People use rockets today to provide the power to send satellites into orbit. Rockets also take lots of equipment far up in the sky. The satellites send back signals for people to study. They help people understand things about our air, our planet, the stars, and other planets. By using rockets, we can "see" things that are far away.

In 1961 we began using rockets to send people on flights into orbit. Someday rockets may take people to Mars and the other planets.

When Jan had finished reading, she could hardly wait to tell her classmates about rockets. So on Monday morning Jan went to see Mr. Kelly right away.

"This is really a good book," Jan said to Mr. Kelly. "I think everyone would enjoy reading it."

"You must have enjoyed it very much yourself," said Mr. Kelly.

"Oh, yes," said Jan. "Do you think we might study rockets as a class project? We could all read this book and look for others, too. We might make a model of a rocket. That would really be interesting."

"I'll be speaking about rockets today in class," said Mr. Kelly. "I'll ask the members of the class if they would like to make a model rocket."

"What fun!" said Jan. "Let's fasten our safety belts and get this project going!"

Illustration by Marie DeJohn

The Night People and the Sun

Irene R. Tamony

In a time long ago, there was a story about life before the sun shone over every land. There were the Night People and the Day People. The Night People camped in a spot where it was night all the time. They liked the darkness because things were always restful and easy. But they longed for some sun, too. The sun would make life exciting in a way different from the stars. The sun would let them garden and do different things.

At last one of the Night People said, "Things can't go on as they always have. We must think of a way to make life better for all of us. We need some sun and the Day People need some darkness. We must get some light for our land."

Adapted from the book *Indian Tales*, by Irene R. Tamony. Copyright © 1968, by Bell & Howell Company.

The Night People called the leaders to a meeting. "Camping in a land far away are the Day People who have a big bright ball called the sun. When they pass the sun back and forth, it lights up their land. We must try to pass our stars back and forth in the same way."

"Yes, yes!" yelled the Night People. "We will try to play this game of the Day People. Then we'll take our stars and seek the land of the sun."

"I camped with the Day People on my travels," said one Night Woman named Ibon. "I will teach you to play the game of the sun. Then our best players can go to seek the sun."

In a short time the best players left for the land of the Day People. The rest of the Night People clapped at the sight of the players going off to seek the sun.

As they got near the land of the Day People, the players could see the bright ball being passed back and forth. The Night People began to play their game with the stars. The best player called to the Day People, "Let me play. Kick the ball to me." And they did.

The Night People passed the stars to the Day People. The leader of the Night People said, "We need the light of the sun. And the Day People need the restful light of our stars."

The Day People agreed. But they needed a way to share the light. Where was the best spot to keep the light?

The Night People sent a player to stand on a hill with the sun. And the Day People sent a player to another hill with the stars. But there still wasn't much light. Then they hung the balls of light on some very tall trees, but there still wasn't much light.

At last Ibon of the Night People picked up the sun and held it tightly in her hands. Then she kicked it with all her might. Up, up, up it went into the sky. There it has stayed to this day, along with the stars, shedding light on every land.

Illustration by Marie DeJohn

road

toad

load

loaf

soap

soak

croak

rode	toad	load	soap
road	load	loaf	soak
toad	loaf	soap	croak

Thinking About Frogs

On the way home from a hike one day, Ted and Dan went past a little lake. There were frogs hopping from the bank into the lake. Several frogs lay on logs to soak up the sun.

Ted said, "I think it would be fun to be a frog. You wouldn't have problems. You could just sit and soak in the sunlight all day."

"Somehow I don't think it would be as simple as that," said Dan. "You'd have to be careful to stay away from some of the other animals. Do you want to sit by the lake for a bit?"

"OK," said Ted. "We still have loads of time to get back."

"Last year," said Dan, "Jan and I went to a lake that had hundreds of frogs. We'd watch those frogs all day long. Jan liked to watch them sit on logs and soak up the sun. But I liked to watch them jump. Wow! Their back legs are so big! One second they're just sitting in the sunshine, and the next second they seem to be flying off along the road! It can startle you if you don't expect it."

Just then a big frog croaked. "That is a good way of speaking to each other," said Ted. "I suppose all the other frogs in the lake understood that croak!"

Then Dan said, "I remember one time Jan and I tried to catch a big frog along the road. We tried everything, but it always jumped just when we reached for it. We chased it over to a pond. What a chase! I went for one last try and landed right in the pond. I was soaked to the skin! That frog got away, and it took a lot of soap and water to get me clean. I was going to brag to everyone at school about having such a big frog for a pet. Well, I didn't have a thing to brag about!"

"I'll bet you were a funny sight!" said Ted.

"Well, that's the last time I tried to catch a frog," said Dan. "I think we'd better start for home now. We're having meat loaf for dinner tonight. And I'd be real upset if I didn't get home in time for meat loaf!"

"OK," said Ted, "let's go. But be careful you don't slide into that frog pond today! If you do, you'll have to soak yourself in soap and water before you can get to that meat loaf!"

Frogs and Toads

This story will tell you some facts about frogs and toads. It will also tell you how frogs and toads are alike and how they are different.

The eggs of frogs and toads are laid in water, where they soak. A female frog lays hundreds of eggs at one time. The eggs look like a mass of little specks. Each jellylike speck has a spot in the middle.

Little animals that look like fish hatch from the soaked eggs. These fishlike animals are called tadpoles or polliwogs. They have long tails, and they eat plants.

Each tadpole wiggles away to be by itself. It keeps getting bigger. As its body gets bigger, it changes. A little frog or toad begins to appear. Swellings at the sides of the tail get longer until they become back legs. Then the tail disappears. The frog tadpole is now a frog, and the toad tadpole is a toad.

Frogs and toads are alike in some ways, but they are different in others. This is how you can tell a toad from a frog. A toad is flatter than a frog, and its back legs are shorter. It has dull, dry, dusty-looking skin with spots. The frog has green skin with black spots or stripes, and it looks wet and shiny all the time.

The toad likes to stay on dry land. And because it doesn't like sunshine, it hides in the daytime under rocks and in the shade. At night it likes to hop along on dusty roads or on paths in the woods. On the other hand, frogs like to soak in water, and they like sunshine best. So they spend a lot of time by ponds and lakes, sitting on a log in the sun or on a leaf in the water.

One other way frogs differ from toads is that frogs have teeth. Toads do not.

Frogs and toads are very helpful to people. They catch lots of insects that might be harmful to people. Toads help by eating insects that are harmful to plants in our gardens.

coat

boat

goat

float

roast

boast

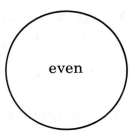

even

road	boast	coat	load
roast	boat	goat	loaf
boast	coat	float	float

River Crossing

All the school children had helped in a drive to save paper and glass. A speaker had asked the boys and girls not to waste these things. They could be saved and used a second time. Or they could even be made into something different.

Mr. Kelly was quite pleased. His class had collected more paper and glass than the rest of the school, but they did not boast. He said, "Because you did such a good collecting job, I'd like to take you on a trip. Ask your moms and dads if you may go to Twisting River Park for a boat ride and a picnic. We'll go by bus a week from today."

The day of the trip was sunny and hot. When the class got off the bus at the river, they left their coats with the driver. "I'll take care of the coats, but don't forget your lunches," he said.

The class followed Mr. Kelly to the boat dock. "We'll take a boat across the river to the park. Then we can hike along the trails there before we eat."

The air by the river felt cold to Milly. "I think I'll go back for my coat," she said. Everyone agreed to wait for Milly to get her coat. At last she came back, and they all jumped on the boat.

The children sat on deck chairs as the boat took them across the river. Some of the girls and boys kept jumping up to see better. Then some of them went to the side and hung over the rail.

Mr. Kelly didn't like that at all. He asked them to go back to their chairs. "I want all of you to get home safely," he said. "I don't think you'd float very long if you fell into the water."

Mr. Kelly told the class about the things they were seeing. He helped them name the different trees and plants along the river and the birds flying over the boat. The class had some very good lessons in their floating "school."

When the boat docked on the far side of the river, the class rushed ashore. They were so hungry Mr. Kelly could tell they wanted to eat right away and go hiking after lunch.

Then the teacher led the way to a lunch stand. As a surprise, he got roasted peanuts and cold drinks for everyone. The class sat in the shade to eat the peanuts with the lunches they had packed. Everything tasted so good!

After lunch Mr. Kelly said, "We must clear off these picnic benches. We want the next people to have a clean spot to eat." He was very pleased by the way everyone pitched in to help. In a short time the park was neat and clean. Then they all set off on a long hike.

Later, back on the bus, Fred said, "Last night Dad said he hoped we'd have a good time. We really did. Thank you for taking us, Mr. Kelly. I think the best part was the ride on the riverboat."

"Yes, crossing the river was fun," said Mr. Kelly. "It makes me think of a good story about dreams. Let me tell it to you."

Then the class settled back in the bus to hear Mr. Kelly's story.

That's What Dreams Are Made Of

All of a sudden there I was, sailing a boat across the water. But how did I get here and where was I going? I was all alone and a little scared, too. I wanted so much to be back home in Beachwood, Texas.

The boat bobbed and rocked and skimmed across the water until at last it came to shore. I stepped from the boat onto the land. There right in front of me was a steep, grassy hill. It blocked my path. I would have to go over it to get to the other side. So

I started up. Up and up I went. I passed a big goat munching on some grass. At last I reached the top. From the peak of that hill I looked far and wide over the land. Beachwood, Texas, was nowhere in sight.

Luckily for me, the other side of the hill was a long, slick, shiny slide, just like a slide at a carnival. So I slid to the bottom. I landed with a thud—right in the middle of a deep, dark, silent forest. Being lost was making me very hungry. So I picked peaches, bananas, roasted nuts, and a peanut butter and jelly sandwich from the trees. The sandwich was so dry I just about choked! But I was right under a tree that dripped milk from its branches. So I took a drink from it.

After I had eaten my meal, I went deeper into the dark forest. On and on I went. My feet were getting sore, and I could barely see. Then, just as I was going to take a rest, I spotted something shining in a clearing. As I crept closer to it, I could see the shiny thing was a rocket ship. Before I could think about where it had come from, I was inside it. I was going up, up, up—and that was really scary.

I landed on Mars, which is not a bad planet, you understand. I just did not care to be there at the moment. I wanted to be home. I stood on top of a crater and looked far and wide. All I could see was darkness and spots of light. There wasn't even a hint of Beachwood, Texas.

Just as I was thinking how silly this was, I started to float. I floated past bright, blazing comets, past the Milky Way and the Big Dipper. A falling star fell past me and, secretly, I made a wish.

"I wish I may, I wish I might,

Get back home sometime tonight."

I floated on past hilltops and treetops and back to nowhere. By this time I was mad! I was tired! I wanted to be home! I was going to scream! But then I woke up.

The sun was shining brightly in my window. "Good morning, sleepy!" my father said to me. "Time to rise and shine, or you'll be late for school."

I sat up. I was home in my bed in Beachwood, Texas. Then I giggled and said to myself, "It never happened! It never happened!" I had not sailed a boat across the water or gotten lost in a forest or taken a rocket ship to Mars. Why, I had not even left my bedroom, and that was the best part of all!

Illustration by James Watling

Dreams

Dreams are made of fairy-tale things
Like goblins, monsters, queens, and kings.
But dreams can be as real as real
About the things we do and feel.

Dreams are made of wishes and hopes,
Of secrets we keep within us.
Some are of anger, some of fear,
Or whatever the night might bring us.

Dreams are gloomy; dreams are bright.
They're made of wind and dark and light.
Dreams are the stories we can't keep.
Dreams are made of fast asleep.

cent

center

cell

cedar

city

circle

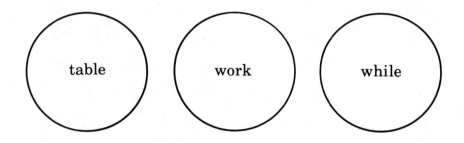

tell	sent	sit	need
sell	cent	city	seed
cell	center	circle	cedar

Ling Center

When summer came, Jan and Dan and the rest of the children on Grove Street had their days free. They were having a good summer.

Then one day Mr. and Mrs. Benton, Jim, and Kim went to visit Mr. Benton's brother. Then Linda and Jane went to summer camp, and Pam, Ted, and Sam went to visit their grandparents. Dan and Jan were left all alone.

Dan and Jan didn't want to be lonely. Sometimes they went to the supermarket while their mom was still at work. Dan liked the market. It had neat stacks of things for sale. There were tea bags, pretzels, and mixes in boxes of all sizes. Next came the eggs, the butter, and the milk. Then there were shelves with jars of peanut butter and jars of jelly. In the center of the market were bins of fresh greens and baskets of grapes. And near the exit were hams and fresh and frozen fish.

Near the front of the store were the apples, peaches, and bananas. One day Dan and Jan picked up one apple and one banana. Then they got in line to pay for them. While they were standing in line, Dan reached into his pocket. "I don't have a cent!" he said in surprise. So Jan paid for both the apple and the banana.

On the way to the market, Dan and Jan had to go along Cedar Street. Each of the old homes on this street had wide stone steps in front and a big yard in back. The house Dan liked best looked like the rest, but it wasn't a family's home. It was a club for boys and girls.

Long ago this house had belonged to a family named Ling. One day Mrs. Ling had said to her husband, "The children on this block need a big, safe spot to play. They need a spot that belongs to just them. You and I don't need such a big house. We could take an apartment in the center of the city. Then we could let the city use this house for a children's club." That's how Ling Center began.

Every time Dan and Jan passed Ling Center, they liked to look in. Boys and girls played checkers and chess at tables inside, while some played basketball in the backyard. Some of the children sat in small circles and did craft work. Others played volleyball, swung on swings, or jumped rope in the driveway. They all seemed to be having such fun.

One day Dan and Jan started for the market. As they passed Ling Center, Jan peeked inside. Dan said, "Jan, would you like to be a member of the Ling Center Club and come here this summer? It's not far from home."

Jan really wanted to do that, so she and Dan went inside to speak to the girl who was working at the table. The girl smiled at Dan and Jan as she asked, "May I help you?"

"Yes," said Jan. "My name is Jan Bell, and I'm from Grove Street. I'd like to be a member of the Ling Center Club."

The girl smiled and said, "My name is Jean. We will be glad to have you as a member of the club."

Then she asked Dan, "Would you like to be a member, too? It won't cost you a cent!"

"Yes, I would," said Dan.

"Do you think your mom or dad could help with the games while you're here? We need all the help we can get," she said.

"I'll bet Dad would help with baseball," said Jan, "and Mom is good at basketball."

So Dan and Jan played at Ling Center all that summer. Mr. and Mrs. Bell came to help with the games and crafts one night a week. They really liked working with everyone at the center. And the people at the center were glad to have Mr. and Mrs. Bell with them.

At the end of the summer, all the mothers and fathers helped to plan a picnic in the park. There were all sorts of games and prizes. After that came hot dogs and hamburgers and cold drinks. The members of the Ling Center Club had really liked their summer of fun!

The Little Old City

One day at school Miss Black spoke to her class. "The big city near here was a much smaller city when it began a hundred years ago. Who has seen the homes in the old part of the city?"

Not one of the children had seen the old part of the city, so Miss Black planned to take the class there. The school was fifteen miles away, so they had to take a bus to get there. When they got to the city, the driver still drove on and on. At last they came to a small park near a river. The streets ending at the river had lots of old shops and old houses.

Miss Black said, "This city is one hundred years old this week. You can see how big it is now, but it all began right here at this park on the river."

"Look," said Tam. "The park is shaped like a circle, and so is the street we're riding on. The rest of the streets all start from this one. They are like the spokes on my bike."

"Yes," said Miss Black. "The people who planned this city wanted some parks. They made one that was shaped like a circle, just as you see it today. It was named River Park, and the street we are on was named River Street. The streets that start from this street are named for the trees that used to be here. They are Pine Street, Cedar Street, Oak Street, and Chestnut Street. Lots of houses on these streets still look the way they did long ago. The families try very hard to keep their homes that way. We'll go inside the ones that are open to the public, and we'll go past the old jail on the way."

The old jail was on Cedar Street. It was locked, and the class had to stretch to peek into the windows of the small, empty cells. "It isn't used these days," Miss Black said. "The jail is old and the cells are too small. The city plans to fix it up so that visitors can go inside. But that work won't be finished until next year."

Later that day the class visited some homes on Cedar Street. People staying in each home told visitors about life long ago. They wore dresses, coats, and pants from times long past. In the bedrooms, the beds and chests and rocking chairs all looked quite small. The old-time kitchens had copper pots and pans sitting on wooden tables. In one room a table was set with dishes and candlesticks a hundred years old. A man lit the candles for the class, and Tam said, "It's still as dark as night in here. I like things much better the way we have them now."

At last they all went to a little shop on Chestnut Street. Miss Black said, "The things here look old, but they really aren't. They are just made to look old so when you look at them at home you will remember this old city. We don't have a lot of time to look at the things. We must start back in a little while."

Tam looked at a number of things. She looked at a little candlestick and some little chairs. At last she chose a little glass pitcher for fifty cents. Then she took a snapshot of one of the old houses. "Mom and Dad like old houses," she said. "When they see this, they'll want to see this old city, too. Then I can take them to see everything I have seen today!"

nice

rice

price

ice

face

Grace

place

space

spruce

bacteria

laugh

night
nice
rice

rice
price
ice

fade
face
Grace

place
space
spruce

Pam's Shopping Song

When I'm sad, not glad at all,
I get on my jacket and stand in the hall
And yell, "I'm going shopping.
Do you want to come?"
My dad yells back, "Mopping?
But I just did some."

I say, "No, no, *shopping*.
I'm all set to go."
My dad says, "Corn popping?
More popcorn? Thanks, no."

I say, "No, no, *shopping*.
We need things to eat."
My dad says then, "Hopping?
No thanks, dear, I'm beat."

Then I run in and hug him
And we laugh so hard
And then we go shopping—
What a nice get-well card!

From Shopping List to Kitchen

When Pam and her father do the marketing, Mr. Sands takes a shopping list. As he drops each thing into the shopping cart, he checks his list. One day when he had finished his shopping at the market on Spruce Street, his list looked like this:

✓eggs	✓bananas
✓milk	✓lemons
✓butter	✓soap
✓cheese	✓cornflakes
✓jelly	✓peaches
✓peanut butter	✓peas
veal	✓corn
✓chicken	✓tea bags
✓frozen crabmeat	✓green beans
✓rice	✓ice tray

Grace, the checker, began to ring up the prices of Mr. Sands's order. She was nearly finished when Mr. Sands said, "Don't forget to add in the price of that apple Pam is eating, Grace. I think it is twenty cents."

Just then Pam looked at their shopping list. She tapped her father on the arm and said, "You didn't get the veal, Dad. It isn't checked off your list."

"That's right," Mr. Sands said with a frown on his face. "The price is up today. We'll just have to eat the meat loaf I made yesterday in place of veal."

Mr. Sands cashed a check to pay for everything, and Grace packed the things in big bags. Then Pam and her father started for home.

When they got home, they took the bags right to the kitchen. Pam liked to unpack the things. She and her dad laughed and chatted as she handed him the boxes, jars, and cartons. He set them in the right places in the cabinets. Then Pam flattened the bags and made a nice pile. Whenever they needed a bag for trash, they could take one from the pile. And the pile didn't take up too much space.

Pam and her dad had a small kitchen with very little shelf space. They were careful to keep each thing in its place. This helped to keep the kitchen looking neat.

Things like crackers, jelly, pretzels, and peanut butter went on the bottom shelves. Then Pam could reach them when she wanted a snack. The boxes of rice and cornflakes went on the top shelves. Some things had to be kept in jars so insects couldn't get at them. The frozen things and the filled ice tray had to be kept in the freezer.

When Pam got to the last bag, she said, "Now I need a place for the milk, butter, and cheese. Ms. Winters says it's better not to let them get hot."

"Did she tell you why?" asked her dad.

"Well," said Pam, "we had a lesson about milk and butter last week in school. Ms. Winters printed some facts on charts and gave us each a chart to keep in a notebook. Wait a second. I'll get mine, and you can read it."

"All right," said her dad. Then he laughed and added, "But you read it, and I'll listen."

Pam got her notebook from her room so she could explain the chart to her dad.

Milk, Cream, and Butter

Here are the facts Pam began to read to her father from the chart in her notebook.

From the Farm to the Dairy

When cattle on a farm are milked, the milk runs into tubes or pipes that take it to a tank. Here the milk is chilled right away.

In a little while a big truck stops at the farm to get the milk. Long hoses take the milk from the farm tank to the milk tank of the truck. Then the trucks take the milk to a dairy in the city.

Farmers try to keep the milk clean, but it is not yet safe to drink. Some small things called bacteria get into milk. Bacteria are so small we can't see them, but they can be quite harmful to us. It is the dairy's job to kill these bacteria.

At the dairy, milk is heated and kept very hot for at least fifteen seconds. This kills the bacteria.

Then the milk is chilled quickly. It is then safe to drink if we keep it cool.

Care of Milk

Milk will not be good to drink if it is left on the table on a hot day. It will also collect smells from other things if it is not kept closed. So remember—keep milk cool and keep it tightly closed.

Things We Get From Milk

If milk is not mixed well at the dairy, the cream will rise to the top. This cream can be skimmed off and used in lots of ways. The dairy can take all the cream from the milk and sell just the skim milk, or the cream can be used to make butter. To make butter, the dairy must beat or churn the cream. The part that is left is called buttermilk.

How We Get Milk

Photo by Vicki J. Basham

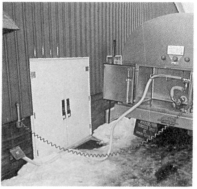

Photo by Vicki J. Basham

1. Cattle are milked. The milk runs into a tank and is chilled.

2. A milk truck collects the milk and takes it to a dairy.

Photo Courtesy of Borden, Inc.

Photo by J. C. Allen & Son, Inc.

3. At the dairy the milk is heated to kill bacteria.

4. The milk is then chilled and safe to drink.

tackle

ankle

tinkle

jingle

juggle

chuckle

tumble

ruffle

(circus)　　　(town)

tack	tackle	tinkle	juggle
tackle	ankle	jingle	chuckle
tinkle	ruffle	juggle	tumble

45

Circus Time!

Mr. Russ Hill had a house on Nineteenth Street, but he visited on Grove Street quite a lot. All the children called him Uncle Russ because he was so nice to them. He wasn't a real uncle to them, but he was as much fun as a real uncle.

One day Uncle Russ came to Grove Street. The boys and girls were glad to see him. They all wanted to ask him about the circus. It was supposed to start in just a week.

Every year the circus came to town. A big tent was set up in an empty lot. Tall, thick poles held it in place. Inside the tent were hundreds of seats in a big circle, and in the middle were three big rings. Three different acts would go on in these rings, all at the same time.

Because Uncle Russ had seen the circus, the children asked him lots of different things about it. At last Uncle Russ said, "Who wants to go to the circus with me next week?"

"We all do!" they yelled.

"Well, I suppose that's settled," chuckled Uncle Russ. "We'll go next week."

So one night a week later, they all piled into Uncle Russ's car and set off for the circus. When they got there, Uncle Russ wanted to keep everyone together, so he asked them to stay close. Then he looked for seven seats near the center ring. At last he got seats he liked. "I think this is the best place to sit," he said. "You can see what happens in all three rings from here. If you get to the circus late, you have to sit near one of the exits. You just can't see as much from those seats."

Just then a woman with bags of peanuts went by. She was calling, "Get your fresh roasted peanuts here! Just fifty cents a bag!"

Uncle Russ chuckled and said, "Well, it's not much of a circus unless you have peanuts!" He called to the woman. "We'll each have a bag of peanuts, please," he said.

She gave him seven bags of peanuts. "That will be three dollars and fifty cents," she said.

As Uncle Russ was paying her, the circus band began to play a lively song. Clowns came running into the tent from all sides. Their faces were painted to make them look happy or sad. One of them had a little umbrella with red and green ruffles on it. He had stiff red and green ruffles at his ankles and his neck, too. He danced in circles until he would tumble down. Then he would get up and start all over. At last he plopped down and waited for the next clown to appear.

The next clown was dressed in rags to look like a tramp. He had the biggest feet the people had ever seen. Each time he took a step, he stumbled and fell. And each time he picked himself up, the clown in back of him tackled him by the ankles and made him tumble down. This went on until the clown who looked like a tramp got away at last.

In the middle of the chase a clown dressed as a fire fighter ran in. He was clanging a big fire bell.

After him came ten clowns riding on a teeny fire truck. One of them jumped off the truck and grabbed a fire hose. She turned it on the clown and soaked him from top to bottom.

One clown had a trained puppy barking at her heels. The puppy ran between the clown's legs and tripped her. Then it ran up to the clown with the umbrella and took it away from him. Then all the clowns tried to tackle the puppy!

The crowd yelled and giggled at all the funny things the clowns did. One boy said, "Uncle Russ, I think that's the best act in the circus!"

"So do I!" said the others.

But Uncle Russ said, "Just wait till you see the next act! It should be the horses! Here they come! Do you hear their bells jingle?"

The band then began to play a song that was different from the clowns' song. Into the ring came three horses, black as coal. Little bells tinkled on each harness.

A woman or man was sitting on each horse. The horses didn't have saddles, so the men and women rode bareback. They just held onto the harnesses. After riding in a circle, they stood up on the horses' backs. Then each one held the harness with the left hand and waved with the right one. Next they began to jump off the horses and jump right back on. And all the while the bells on the harnesses tinkled and jingled in time with the band.

When the act was over, Jan clapped and clapped. "I like the horses best!" she said.

"Just wait till you see the rest of the acts!" said Uncle Russ.

But Jan didn't hear him, because she was looking at a side ring. In it a man had begun to juggle red balls in the air. He had five, then seven, then nine, all in the air at the same time. Next he juggled rings and dishes, but he never dropped one! Then he kept ten plates spinning on a table while he juggled the rings in the air. It was hard to stop looking at him.

In the center ring, a trained seal began to do its act. The seal balanced a ball on the tip of its nose and made the ball turn and turn. Then the seal went up three steps and did all sorts of tricks at the top. After each trick, the seal used its flippers to clap for itself. The trainer gave the seal a small fish each time. Then the seal barked as if to say, "Thank you!"

In the end ring a woman was turning balls into apples and apples into birds. As she reached for the birds, they turned into flags!

The acts seemed to get better and better. At last there was one big act with all the animals, clowns, women, and men at the same time. The band played its last number, and Uncle Russ said, "Well, that's it!"

Everyone seemed dizzy because they had seen such sights. Uncle Russ jingled some money in his pocket. "How about some lemonade? It's just forty cents a glass!"

So they stopped at a lemonade stand. They had to wait in line for some time, but the lemonade really tasted good when they got it. By the time they had finished their lemonade, the parking lot was nearly empty. It was not hard to see Uncle Russ's brown car. They all ran and piled into it.

As Uncle Russ got into the car, all the children began at the same time. "Thank you, Uncle Russ!" they said. "That was an exciting day! We can't wait for the circus to come back to town!"

beetle

steeple

bugle

title

idle

maple

giant

cube	ride	beet	steep
bugle	idle	beetle	steeple
maple	title	needle	beetle

A Trip to the Park

When school began in September, the people from Ling Center began to meet after school and on weekends. One Sunday a number of the children were able to take a bus trip to a nearby state park.

The maple trees in the park had just begun to turn red. They looked very bright with the tall, dark pine trees in back of them. The pine needles on the paths smelled good.

Everyone liked the big rocks and the caves in the park. They also liked the names for all the different places. People had named one very tall, sharp rock Steeple Rock. Another rock was shaped rather like a bugle at one end, so it was called Funny Man's Bugle.

A big, flat rock in the middle of a stream was named Giant Beetle. When Pam looked at it, she said, "Giant Beetle is staring at me!" She was just pretending. But it really did look that way.

After looking at the rocks, the people from Ling Center spotted some stone steps. They followed the steps into a set of caves. The top cave was quite big. It was called Ash Cave because it had ashes in it from fires made long ago. Linda said it wouldn't be a bad place for a home, but she wouldn't want to stay there forever. Pam said it would be scary to be in the cave alone.

When they left Ash Cave, they looked for a good place for lunch. In the center of some maple trees was a spot with fireplaces for people to use. No one was idle. While Pam and Linda made lemonade, the dads and moms cooked hot dogs and hamburgers. Ted and Kim placed a napkin, a plastic cup, and a plate on the table for each person. Then they heaped buns on another plate. It was a very good lunch for some very hungry people.

After lunch they packed up their things and took a long hike. It was just beginning to get dark when they got back onto the bus and started for home. On the way, they made up songs and their titles. They called one "The Bugle Boy." The title of another was "Steeple Chase." Then they made up a song about the rock Pam liked best. As you might suppose, the title of that song was "Pam and the Giant Beetle."

By the time the bus reached Ling Center, darkness had fallen. As the sleepy children got off the bus, they agreed to plan another trip. "I just hope the next trip is as exciting as this one!" said Pam. "What a day we had!"

Illustration by Marie DeJohn

The Woman in the Big Brick House

When Peg and Peter Jones came to Crossbend to visit their Uncle Dave, there was gossip all over town about the woman in the big brick house. The woman's name was Emma Crane. She had come to Crossbend three years before. For some reason the people in the town didn't like her very much. "She thinks she's better than we are," people would say. "She's always idle. And she never leaves that house or has visitors."

"Why do they say Mrs. Crane is mean if they've never met her?" Peg asked her uncle.

"Some people like to gossip," Uncle Dave said. "But you shouldn't listen to them."

The big brick house looked quite nice. There were pink and red roses and tall maple trees in the yard. Peg just couldn't understand why people said bad things about Mrs. Crane. Each time Peg passed the house, she would think about the woman who was inside.

One day as Peg and Peter were picking grapes from Uncle Dave's grapevines, Peg asked, "Peter, why do you suppose people don't like Mrs. Crane?"

"You've got me," Peter said as he snapped grapes from one of the vines. "But I think you'd better forget about Mrs. Crane."

Still, Peg wouldn't forget it. She wanted to meet Mrs. Crane before she and Peter went back home.

"I have a plan," Peg began. "Will you help me?"

"What sort of plan?" Peter asked. He could always tell when his sister was up to something.

"Well," said Peg, "do you think Mrs. Crane is really as mean as people say?"

"Oh, no!" groaned Peter. "Are you thinking about Mrs. Crane?"

"It could be that she's just shy and lonely," Peg said. "Maybe someone should try being nice to her. Would you be afraid to meet her?"

"No," Peter said as he plucked a beetle from the grapevine.

"Then you'll go with me to her house," Peg said quickly. "We can take her some grapes."

"I didn't say that!" said Peter.

"Please, Peter," Peg begged.

Peter looked at his sister for a long time. "Oh, all right," he said at last. Then he smiled. "I suppose you want to go right now."

"Yes," said Peg as she picked up her bucket of grapes. Then she and Peter started for Mrs. Crane's house.

When they got to the gate of the big house, Peg said, "Look, the gate isn't even locked."

They went into the yard and started up the drive, but suddenly Peg got just a little scared. Suppose Mrs. Crane was as mean as everyone said? What would she say if she thinks Peter and Peg are sneaking up to her house?

At last they reached the steps. "Well, go on, ring the bell," Peter said to Peg.

Peg was shaking as she went up the steps. "You don't suppose she'll have us sent to jail for trespassing, do you?" Peg asked.

"It's too late to think about that now," Peter said. "Ring the bell."

Peg rang the bell. Then she nearly tripped as she stomped back down the steps to stand beside her brother. They held hands and waited until someone called.

"Who's there?" It was a woman who spoke. Peg and Peter looked to the side of the house. A woman with a cane was coming their way. She wasn't smiling.

"Are you Mrs. Crane?" Peg stammered.

"I am," the woman said. "Who are you, and what are you doing here?" She still wasn't smiling.

"We're Peg and Peter Jones," Peg said. "We wanted to bring you some grapes."

The woman tapped her cane and came closer. She said, "You weren't afraid to come here?"

"We just wanted you to feel welcome in Crossbend," Peter said as he handed her the grapes.

Mrs. Crane looked at the bucket of grapes. Then, to their surprise, she smiled. "And such a nice welcome," she said and took the grapes. Then Peg and Peter smiled, too.

After that the people of Crossbend felt ashamed for all the things they had said about Mrs. Crane. They had a big picnic so they could meet her.

Everyone was happy that day. But no one was as happy as Peg and Peter Jones. Their summer visit had ended, but so had the gossip about the woman in the big brick house.

Illustration by Marie DeJohn

ledge

edge

dodge

judge

budge

ridge

bridge

build

rid	cot	led	bud
ridge	cod	ledge	budge
bridge	dodge	edge	judge

Risky Work on a Bridge

"Look, Mom!" called Manny Santis as he and his mother drove across Ben Franklin Bridge. "Three people are painting the top of that bridge!"

"I can't stop now," said Dr. Santis, "but I'll park on the other side. Then we can look."

Dr. Santis parked on Ridge Street. They went back to the edge of the river to look at the painters working on the bridge.

"I'm glad you have a safe job, Mom," said Manny. "It can't be very safe painting a bridge."

"Working on a bridge is fairly safe if the people are well trained," said Dr. Santis. "I came past here every day when the bridge was being built. Sometimes I stopped just to look at the people working. Each person seemed to understand the job very well. Each did the work and helped the others who were also working."

"But it wouldn't be safe for people who get dizzy at the top of a building or a ladder," said Manny.

"That's so," said his mom. "Those ledges and beams are not very wide. They're not safe for people who are likely to get dizzy. But if you're trained to work on a ledge, you can do it safely."

She went on, "It's really the same at a circus. The people doing the acts at the top of the tent are well trained, so they are safe."

"And it's the same for people who paint tall houses or even steeples," said Manny.

Then his mom said, "The builders who worked on the bridge had quite a scare one day. A man working at the top dropped a small hammer. He yelled to the workers under him. They all wore steel helmets, but a falling hammer could still hurt one of them. When you're working on a bridge, you can't duck or dodge. So they just held on tight with their arms and legs and didn't budge one bit."

"Did it hit one of them?" Manny asked in alarm.

"No. One of the workers felt the hammer brush her arm. But it kept falling and hit the edge of a small boat in the river. It smashed the edge of the boat as if the boat were hit by a sledgehammer."

Dr. Santis went on, "That night the woman who felt the hammer brush her was on TV. She said she never blamed people when things like that happened at work."

The woman on TV said, "I could be the next one to drop something. You just have to remember not to budge when it happens. You can't dodge a falling hammer when you're standing on a ledge. That's why you must keep your helmet on at all times. These risks are all in a day's work."

"The date the bridge was finished is marked on this ledge," Manny's mom added. "It took three years to build it from start to finish."

"Will it take long to paint it?" asked Manny.

"Well, not nearly as long as it took to build it, I would judge," said Dr. Santis.

On the way home, Manny looked for bridges. "Maybe I'll build bridges one day!" he said to himself.

Bridges

It's hard to say when people began to build bridges. Perhaps hundreds of years ago someone needed to cross a stream. That person may have seen a log that had fallen across the stream. The person then used the log to get to the other side.

Then perhaps people felt a need for a better way to cross the stream. They may have laid a second log beside the one that had fallen. This gave them a wider roadway. They could then drag bigger loads across it. Next, they may have laid more logs or fastened the logs together to fill in the cracks. This made the roadway safer and not as bumpy. This was the timber bridge.

In jungles, vines hung from the trees on the riverbanks. People of long ago might have used these vines to swing across streams. Then they probably began to use thick vines or ropes to make swinging bridges. Rope bridges are still in use in some places.

Today, bridges may be made from wood, stone, steel, or concrete. They may be fixed tightly in place. Some have parts that lift up or swing aside to let big ships pass.

Bridges take people, cars, trucks, and trains quickly across water or land. They cross brooks, rivers, and deep water between towns at the edge of the sea. On dry land, bridges connect one hill with the next to help us save time. Crossing a bridge is much faster than going to the bottom of one hill and then up to the next.

The next time you ride in a bus, train, or car, look for bridges along the way. At each one, ask yourself these things:

Is it made of wood, stone, concrete, or steel?

Why did people build it here?

Was it built to connect hills or to go across water?

Can part of it be raised to let a ship go by?

rage

wage

age

engage

range

change

strange

baby

pound

monkey

rang	range	rag	wag
range	change	rage	wage
change	strange	age	engage

A Name for a Baby

One morning each week, children can get into the Grove City Zoo for just twenty cents. So, late in the summer, Pam's dad drove the Grove Street boys and girls to the zoo.

Dan and Jan had visited the zoo in June. They had seen a baby chimpanzee that was born in the spring. They wanted to see him right away. As soon as the van was parked, the Grove Street kids raced to the chimpanzee cage.

The baby chimpanzee was swinging from a bar inside the cage. He looked just like his mother, who was eating a banana. A pile of green lettuce was still in a pan at one side of the cage.

"Look at the card at the top of the cage," said Dan. "It says 'Baby' and has the date the little chimp was born. You can tell his age from that date. He isn't a baby now, but he still doesn't have another name."

"What a shame!" said Jan. "I think it's time he

had a real name. Let's ask Miss Jones if we can change his name."

"Does Miss Jones take care of the monkeys?" Dan asked.

"These aren't really monkeys, Dan," Gus said. "Monkeys have tails, but these chimps have no tails. They belong to the ape family."

A male chimpanzee was in the cage next to the baby's. He seemed to be the same age as the baby's mother. Tam said, "Did you see that chimpanzee skating on TV last week, Pam? He looked just like this one!"

"Well, it could have been this one, I suppose," said Jan.

A keeper who was working nearby told them, "This chimp doesn't skate on TV. Circus animals are trained to do things like that, but zoo animals aren't."

Suddenly the chimp reached between the bars of the cage for the keeper's cap. The keeper ducked just in time. "I was too fast for you that time!" he said to the chimpanzee.

Then he turned to Gus with a chuckle and said, "I think I'll have to change jobs! These monkeys and apes play tricks all day!" But he really wouldn't change his job, because he liked the animals too much. Besides, the zoo paid its workers good wages.

Then the keeper said, "Look at the orangutan in this cage. You can tell an orangutan by its shaggy hair and fat cheeks."

The orangutan did have fat cheeks and a coat of long red hair. She was a strange sight. Jim wanted to see her swing from the bar or stamp her feet. Tam wanted to see her eat. But the orangutan didn't do a thing. She just sat.

"Is she sick?" asked Linda.

"She just came to the zoo yesterday," said the keeper. "I think she's being so strange because she misses her home and family. But I'd better ask Mr. Hines if we should have Dr. Hall take a look at her."

"Who is Mr. Hines?" asked Kim.

"The zoo engaged Mr. Hines just last week to look after the monkeys and the apes," the keeper said.

"Then we'll send a letter with our name change for the baby chimp to Mr. Hines," said Jan. "If we pick a good name, maybe the zoo people will stop calling him Baby and let him have a real name."

After days and days of thinking, the Grove Street kids had a name to send to Mr. Hines. It was not hard to see the reason for the one they picked.

Then, in the last week of summer, Mr. Hines called Jan at home. He said the people at the zoo had named the baby chimp Grover. That was the name that the children on Grove Street had sent him!

Different Sorts of Apes

Lots of people like monkeys and apes more than all the other zoo animals. Monkeys and apes may be kept in cages in the same part of the zoo. But they are not in the same family. One way to tell them apart is by the tail. Monkeys have tails. Apes do not.

There are a number of different sorts of apes. These are the gorilla, chimpanzee, orangutan, and gibbon.

Gorillas are the biggest of the apes. When they stand upright, they may be six feet tall. On the scales, they may go up to five hundred pounds.

These big apes with long fangs and strange faces can never be tamed. In the jungle, they do not eat meat, but in the zoo they may begin to like it. They can stand upright on their back legs for a short time, but they travel on their hands and feet. At night, they make nests to sleep in.

Chimpanzees are smaller than gorillas and much smarter. They are not hard to train. One farmer is teaching a chimp to drive a jeep.

Orangutans are strange-looking apes with puffy cheeks and long red hair. They range from three to five feet tall.

Gibbons have longer arms than the other apes. In the jungle, they race from treetop to treetop, chattering as they go.

Apes do not always enjoy being kept in zoos. Pages of strange tales are printed about one gorilla named Bamboo who came to a zoo at the age of one. He had good care, but he was never tamed. He seemed to go into a rage whenever people looked at him. Then he would pound his chest with his fists. He would toss all sorts of things at people within range of his cage. Keepers didn't dare go into his cage when he was in such a rage.

Gibbons, too, do not seem to enjoy zoo life. In fact, it is hard to keep them alive in zoos. Maybe they can't stop wishing for the free life they used to have in the treetops. What do you think?

Feelings

feeling
good-bad
not too sad, rather glad
feeling
upside-down
like a frown
ugly-nice
cold as ice
feeling
mixed-up-lonely
can't explain
oh, so strange
feeling
nilly-willy
oh, my, really
such a very silly
feeling
always feeling
feelings

cabbage

luggage

package

damage

image

beverage

manage

vacation

aunt

rug	damage	cab	man
luggage	image	cabbage	manage
damage	beverage	package	manager

An Exchange of Children

Manny's mom and dad were sitting in the yard after dinner. "Summer is nearly over," Dr. Santis said. "Manny will be going back to school, and I don't think he has had much fun on his vacation this year."

"It's not too late," said Mr. Santis. "I think we can manage something. Why don't we have an exchange of children?"

"An exchange of children!" cried Manny's mom. "What do you mean?"

"Oh, the exchange would be for just a week. We could send Manny and Dan to visit Carl and Sandy at their farm," Manny's dad said. "They have told us there are some children near there who would like to visit Grove City. Let's ask them to come here for a week."

"I think Manny would like that," said Dr. Santis. "He has always wanted to spend more time at the farm."

In just a short time the plans were made. Uncle Carl and Aunt Sandy were pleased the boys were coming, and the boys from the farm were happy about going to Grove City.

Manny's mom and dad drove the boys to the bus stop. "You look as if you were going to spend a year on the farm," joked Mr. Santis. "All that baggage for just one week!"

"It isn't all mine," said Manny. "I have a package for Uncle Carl and Aunt Sandy. I have to handle it very carefully. I don't want it to get damaged."

Then the boys got on the bus and waved good-by to Manny's mom and dad. Manny's aunt would meet them at Maple Glen, a town near the farm.

Aunt Sandy and her dog, Kerny, were waiting for the boys at the bus stop. After Aunt Sandy had placed the luggage in the back of the farm truck, Manny said, "This is Dan. He's in my class at school. I told him he would like the farm."

"I hope you both will," said Manny's Aunt Sandy. "Let's get into the truck so we can get your vacation started." Manny, Dan, and Aunt Sandy got into the front of the truck and sat down. Kerny jumped onto the back with the luggage.

"I like Kerny," said Dan. "I have a dog named Rags at home."

At last the truck turned onto the road that led to the farm. There were maple trees lining the road on each side. Because of the trees, Aunt Sandy and Uncle Carl's farm was called Maple Leaf Farm.

Uncle Carl was waiting for them on the steps of the farmhouse. Manny jumped from the truck and ran to hug him.

Suddenly Manny said, "Oh, no, I forgot the package I have for you!" He ran back to the truck just in time. Kerny was sniffing at the box! "It's lucky you didn't damage this!" Manny said to the dog.

Uncle Carl thanked Manny for the package and took it into the house. "Let's have lunch now and look at the gift later," he said.

After lunch, Uncle Carl took the boys to look at the farm. They stopped at the barnyard to see the chickens. A mother cat and her kittens were there, too. At last Uncle Carl and the boys reached a patch of land where sheep were happily grazing.

"This is the best place on the farm," said Manny. "I wish I could take a little lamb with me when I go home."

"I don't think a lamb would manage well in the city," said Uncle Carl. "Wouldn't you rather take one of the kittens? A kitten would be a much better house pet than a lamb."

"All right," said Manny. "I'll ask Mom and Dad the next time we call."

On the way back to the farmhouse, they crossed a little stream. Dan stopped and looked down at the water. "Look, I can see myself in the water," he called to Manny. And there was a clear image of Dan in the stream.

"Look at all the skunk cabbage along the edge of the stream," said Manny. He was pleased he had remembered the name of that plant from another visit.

"Why don't we pick some for dinner?" asked Dan.

"I don't think you'd like the taste of skunk cabbage," said Uncle Carl. "It's very different from the cabbage you've eaten."

Aunt Sandy was sitting on the porch when Uncle Carl and the boys came back. Manny and Dan were glad to see a beverage pitcher on the table. Aunt Sandy said, "I made some iced tea for you."

After they had all had a drink, Aunt Sandy said, "Why don't we open the package from Manny now?" She carefully took off the paper and ribbon and lifted the lid. Inside was a painting. A card on the top said, "Thank you, Aunt Sandy and Uncle Carl."

"How nice!" said Aunt Sandy. "Let's hang it in the front room right now."

When the painting had been hung, they all stood back to look at it. "Thank you, Manny," said Aunt Sandy. "It was so nice of you to do this for us. I think we should exchange children every year!"

bulge

danger
stranger
passenger

carry

future

range	strange	pass	tug
strange	stranger	passed	bug
stranger	danger	passenger	bulge

Litter

Manny and Dan had a very nice visit with Manny's Aunt Sandy and Uncle Carl. It seemed just a short time until the visit was over, and they were on their way back to Grove City. There were lots of other passengers on the bus. A tall girl sat across from Dan and Manny. She was carrying a bag that bulged at the seams. She tossed it onto the rack over the seats.

As they rode along, all the passengers looked at the roadway. Suddenly the stranger said, "Look at that mess! People should be ashamed!"

Dan looked at the stranger. "Are you speaking to me?" he asked.

"Yes," said the girl. "I was just looking at the roadside. Sometimes the hills and rivers look so nice. Then people dump litter all over the place. Look there," she said. "What will our future be like if that sort of littering isn't stopped?"

A huge bag of trash was spilled along the road. "People just don't understand the danger of tossing litter like that," the girl said. "They just don't think of the future!"

"You're right," said Manny. "There are fines for littering, but they don't seem to do much good. There must be something people can do."

"People should carry litterbags in their cars," said the girl. "They could keep their papers and things in them. Then they could empty the litterbags into trash cans when they stop."

"That would be a start," said Manny. "I remember reading a play about litter. It told about the dangers of litter. Maybe we could do it for everyone at school."

Manny, Dan, and the girl began thinking of other things they could do to prevent littering. Can you think of ways you could help?

The Grime Crushers Nab the Litter Monsters

Players: **Spinner**

        Speedy

        Spiff } The Grime Crushers

        Spike

Three Litter Monsters

Spinner has just called the Grime Crushers to an important meeting. Let's listen to what they're saying.

Spinner: All right, gang, we have a big job to perform today. I have an urgent message from Everytown, U.S.A. It states that giant Litter Monsters have invaded the town. Everywhere these monsters go, they leave a path of trash and filth.

Speedy: So the people of Everytown want us to stop these monsters?

Spinner: That's right. Otherwise their parks and lakes will be filthy. They are really alarmed!

Spike: They have a right to be alarmed! But what can we do? There are cards everywhere that say "DO NOT LITTER! ONE HUNDRED DOLLARS FINE!"

Spiff: Maybe Litter Monsters can't read.

Spinner: Oh, they can read all right. Littering is a bad habit with them. They just don't care.

Speedy: And they're too lazy to dump their trash where it belongs.

Spike: So if we're not going to fine them or lock them in jail, what are we going to do?

Spinner: We'll go to Everytown, grab all the monsters, bring them back here, and then carry them off to the Land of the Litter Mess.

Spiff: Oh, no, not the Land of the Litter Mess! I hate that place. The smell makes me sick! Besides, we have to ride in the Future Scanner to get there. And that thing makes me dizzy!

Speedy: Spiff, I'm afraid Spinner is right. The one way to stop these monsters from littering is to let them see a land filled with litter, a land where you can't drink the water or breathe the air.

Spiff: Oh, no.

Spike: Come on, Spiff, be brave. It's the best way to carry off this lesson.

Spinner: OK, gang, we have grime to crush! Let's get those monsters and bring them back here as quickly as we can.

It is evening now and the Grime Crushers are just coming back with their prisoners. (The Grime Crushers enter. They march the Litter Monsters in and line them up.)

Spiff: They don't look like monsters.

Speedy: But they are, Spiff, and they're a danger to us today and in the future.

Spike: Excuse me. Here are the masks for the Grime Crushers. The Future Scanner is all set, so let's be on our way.

(The Grime Crushers and the Litter Monsters file into the Future Scanner.)

Monster 1: Where are you taking us?

Monster 2: Are we in danger?

Monster 3: You aren't going to hurt us, are you?

Spinner: No, we aren't going to hurt you. We are going to carry you into the future.

Speedy: We want you to see what our lives will be like if you keep on littering.

Spike: All set? Close the hatch. Grime Crushers, get those masks on. *(Spiff closes the hatch.)*

Monster 1: Why do you have those masks?

Spiff: You'll see when we get to the Land of the Litter Mess.

Spike: Hang on! *(He presses a button.)* Here we go!

In just seconds the Future Scanner takes its passengers to a place somewhere in the future.

Spinner: Well, here we are, the Land of the Litter Mess. Take a good look, monsters. We don't want you to forget how a land of litter looks.

Spiff: I think I'm going to be sick!

Monster 2: It's such a mess!

Spiff: So smelly!

Monster 3: Just piles and piles of garbage—no trees, no plants. Not one thing is alive here!

Speedy: How could something survive in that mess? Look over there. That lake used to bulge with fresh water and fish. Now it's just filth.

Spiff *(moaning):* I am really going to be sick!

Monster 1: Take us away, please. This is too much!

Spinner: We'll agree to take you back with us *if* you agree to stop your littering.

All Monsters *(raising their right hands)*:

Oh, yes, we agree!

No more littering from us, you'll see.

We'll keep our land litter free!

Spiff: Good! Now let's get away from here. All passengers, back into the Future Scanner!

(Spike presses a button, and the Future Scanner disappears.) Thanks to the Grime Crushers, Everytown, U.S.A., was saved from becoming one big litter mess.

gentle

germ

German

geranium

ginger

giraffe

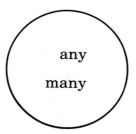

any

many

jet	germ	jingle	gentle
gentle	German	ginger	germ
germ	geranium	giraffe	geranium

Let's Plant a Garden

One day Mrs. Bell stood in the kitchen looking at the backyard. Then she began to frown.

"What's the matter, Dot?" asked Mr. Bell. "Has something upset you?"

"Oh, not really, Tom," she said. "I was just looking at the backyard. It's so plain and drab. It needs something to perk it up. The grass is nice, but we could do more with that yard."

"I think you're right," said Tom. "Dan and Jan have taken good care of the plum tree they planted. Let's see if they would like to plant a garden."

"I'd like that. We could all work on it, and we could plant some flowers along the edges," said Dot. "That could be fun, and the yard would look much nicer."

"And we can eat many of the things we plant," said Tom. "I'll call Dan and Jan so we can start planning."

When Dan and Jan came into the kitchen, their

mother said, "How would you like to plant a garden? I think it would be fun if we all worked on it."

"So do I," said Dan.

"I like flowers," said Jan. "May we plant geraniums?"

"That would be nice," said Dad. "Any flower you like is fine with me. Let's go to the garden center tonight and select our plants."

There were so many plants at the garden center it was hard to pick the ones they wanted. As Jan was looking at the geraniums, a gentlemen in a red jacket came up to her. "May I help you?" he asked.

"There are so many plants," said Jan. "I must be careful to select the right ones. Any geranium just won't do!"

"Yes, it's important to select plants that you'll like," said the man. "Maybe I can help. This is our biggest geranium. It comes from Germany. A woman there worked for many years to bring about this vivid red shade."

"That is a nice geranium. You said it's German," said Jan. "Does it have a name?"

"Yes," said the man, "the woman in Germany called it Ginger because it smells like the spice."

As Jan bent over to pick one of the pots up, he added, "You must be very gentle with these. The stems can snap off quite easily."

"I'll handle them gently," said Jan. "Thanks for your help. Right now I must look for my brother." She set six geraniums in her cart and went to look for Dan. He was looking at the cabbage plants.

"What do you have there?" asked Dan.

"German geraniums," laughed Jan. "And they're named Ginger."

"Geraniums with names?" Dan asked. "That seems strange."

"Maybe so," said Jan, "but I like the name

Ginger. Just think, a geranium named after a spice!"

"Help me pick some cabbage plants. We can plant lots of them. And we'll want to look at seeds for green beans, peas, and lettuce," Dan said.

"How about some corn?" said Jan.

"That takes too much room. We're going to have a small garden," said Dan.

"We'd better look for Mom and Dad to see what they've picked," said Jan.

Mr. and Mrs. Bell had selected lots of plants and seeds. When they looked at everything Dan and Jan had, Mrs. Bell said, "My goodness! I hope we don't have too many things to plant. This is going to be a bigger garden than I was planning."

"But it will be fun," said Dan.

"As well as work!" said his dad.

"We'll be glad we did it," said Mrs. Bell. "Let's get these things home and plant them."

As they started home, Dan began to sneeze. He turned his face away from the others. "Excuse me," he said. "I hope you don't get any of my cold germs."

"We'll be fine," said his father. "Even if we do, we're probably as strong as any cold germs!"

On the way home, they passed the zoo. All they could see from the road was a tall giraffe. "Aren't giraffes neat?" said Dan. "I'll bet that giraffe can see for miles."

When the Bells got home, they took all the plants and seeds from the back of the car. As they carried their things to the yard, Jan said, "I hope our garden will be a nice one."

"It will be," said Dad, "but we'll have to work at it."

That night the Bell family worked in their garden. They raked and dug and yanked up weeds. It took a long time to get all their plants and seeds in the right spots. They were huffing and puffing when they finished. Jan gave her last geranium a gentle pat so it would stand up just so.

"I am so tired," she said.

"We all are," said her dad, "but doesn't our garden look nice?"

"It really does," said Dan. They all stood back for a long look.

"Well, so far, so good," said Jan, "but will our luck last?"

"It's not just luck," said her mom. "We will have to work hard. We'll have to water our garden when it's dry, and we'll have to keep after the weeds."

"What a lot of work!" said Dan. Suddenly, he began to sneeze.

"Come on, Dan," said Mom. "Let's get you and your cold germs to bed."

One night many weeks later, the Bells sat down for dinner. Everything tasted so good—fresh beans and peas and lettuce. Then the family said, "Let's plant another garden next year!"

Spring Garden

In my little garden
By the apple tree,
Daffodils are swaying—
Oh, so playfully!

Daffodils in golden gowns,
Tulips looking bright,
Pansies smiling dreamily—
What a happy sight!

Photo by Aaron Haupt

wrap

wrist

wreck

wrench

write

wrote

wrong

saw

raw

right	peck	rap	
write	wreck	wrap	saw
wrote	wrench	wrist	raw

The Do-It-Yourself Desk

Tam Lee would be going back to school on the seventh of September. Her mother wanted to get her a small desk. Mr. Lee had sprained his wrist a week before, but he said, "Maybe we could build a desk for Tam ourselves. All we need is some lumber and the right tools. My wrist should be all right in a day or so. And we still have five weeks to build the desk."

The next Sunday Mr. Lee saw an ad on TV for a set of tools. The set had a saw, a hammer, a plane, and a wrench. The Lees really needed the wrench, and the set was on sale. The price seemed very good.

The Lee home was not near the store that had the tools on sale. Mr. Lee asked Mrs. Lee, "Are you planning to go downtown this week? You could pick up that tool set."

"No," said Mrs. Lee, "I don't really need anything downtown this week."

"I could write a note to the store," said Mr. Lee.

"I'll write it," said Mrs. Lee. "It must be hard for you to write with your sore wrist."

So Mrs. Lee wrote a letter to the store asking them to send a set of the tools. She enclosed a check with the letter. A week after she had mailed the letter, a truck stopped in front of the house. A driver left a package.

When Mr. Lee opened the package, he saw that the handle of the hammer was split and the wrench was missing. He had to wrap the tools and mail them back to the store. Because his wrist was better, he wrote and enclosed a letter himself. The letter asked if he could still have the tools at sale price.

Late in the next week a second tool set came. This time the wrench was in the box, and the hammer had a strong handle. Nearly three weeks had passed, so Mr. Lee went right to the lumberyard and got the wood to build the desk.

But when he came home and picked up the box

of tools, he saw that it was marked with the wrong price. Mr. Lee didn't want to pay more than sale price for the tools. He wrote to the store and waited a week to hear from them. He didn't want to use the tools until the store wrote to tell him the price of the set. By now it was September.

Mrs. Lee said, "Let's try using our old tools. We have just six days left."

"No," said Mr. Lee, "they might wreck the lumber."

On September second, the Lees got a note from the store. The note said the Lees could have the tools for the sale price. Mr. and Mrs. Lee began to build the desk right away. They had to work very quickly, but they finished the desk the day before Tam went back to school.

When Tam saw her desk, she said, "What a nice surprise! I will do all my homework on my desk."

Then Mr. and Mrs. Lee told her they had made the desk themselves. That made Tam like her desk even more. She took very good care of it so she could use it in the years to come.

The Story of Tools

People of long, long ago had homes in caves. We call these people cave dwellers. These cave dwellers didn't have any tools. When they went hunting, they looked for animals that were not strong or fast.

At last someone made a stone hammer for hunting and fighting. Then these people could catch and kill strong, fast animals. That may be the way toolmaking began.

Next a tool for skinning animals and scraping and cutting hides was needed. A stone with a sharpened edge was used for this work. The cutting tool was probably the second tool to be invented.

Long, thin bits of bone were used to make holes in the hides. One hide could be fastened to another to make a garment. Or many hides could be fastened side by side to make a tent. Someone made a hole in the dull end of a thin bone and invented the needle!

After many years, spears were invented to help people hunt. People saw that cooked meat made a better meal than raw meat. So they made cooking tools. Then they began to plant seeds for crops. So tools for planting were invented.

As time passed, people needed more and more tools for different jobs. They invented the saw, the ax, and the plane to cut and shape wood. They invented the sledgehammer and chisel to cut into stone. They invented wrenches to work with metals, too.

Writing was invented, and people began to read. They needed tools for writing and printing. They made brushes, pens, and ink. As time passed, more and more people became interested in reading. The printing press was invented. Then there were more books for people to read.

Today we have tools for nearly anything we want to do or make. How many different tools can you name? Remember, it all began with that hunter of long ago who invented the stone hammer!

weigh

neighbor

weight

freight

eight

eighth

	weigh weight eight	weight freight eight	eighth eight freight
weigh neighbor			

Good Luck on Eighth Street

Ann Elwood

Maggie was riding her bike on the right side of Eighth Street. "Come on, Jay," she yelled. "I'll race you across the railroad tracks!"

"OK," said Jay, riding hard to catch up.

Just as they got across the tracks, the crossing gate came down. They turned to watch the freight train go by.

Mr. Franco, the gatekeeper, yelled at them, "You got across the tracks just in time! You should be more careful. Eighth Street is no place to ride bikes!"

As Maggie and Jay rode off, Jay said, "Do you think Mr. Franco is mad at us?"

"Yes," said Maggie. "But probably because he's afraid someone will be hurt at that crossing. We should be more careful."

A little later Jay and Maggie were sitting on Jay's

steps. "I wish we had a place for a bike path," Maggie said. "The little kids really need a place to play, too."

"Let's make a playground right here on Eighth Street," said Jay.

"Good luck," said Maggie, meaning she didn't think it could happen.

Just then Mrs. Franco came down the street. She stopped and said, "Good luck?" She shifted the weight of the package she was carrying. "You make good luck for yourself." Then she went into her apartment.

"She's right," Maggie said.

"What about that empty lot down the street?" asked Jay.

"What about it?" asked Maggie.

"It belongs to Mr. and Mrs. Franco," said Jay. "They might let us use it if we could get the money to turn it into a playground."

"We'll have bake sales and car washes. And we could ask the neighbors to chip in. With the money we make, we could get playground things," Maggie added.

"And make a bike path!" said Jay.

Their plans went well. Mr. Franco said they could use his lot. So they collected money from the neighbors and had a bake sale and three car washes. All in all, they made one hundred and eight dollars.

The day after the last car wash, Maggie and Jay went to the empty lot. They had a little book that told about playground things you could send away for. They added up the prices of the things they wanted. Then Jay saw a line in the back of the book. It said, "Freight costs must be added."

They checked the weight of each thing they wanted to get. Then they added the freight costs to their list of prices. It came to much more than one hundred and eight dollars. "We can't go back to the neighbors," said Jay. "I don't want to ask them for more money."

Just then Mr. Franco came along from his job at the freight yard. "Problems?" he asked.

They told him about the money. "The things we want weigh too much," said Maggie. "We need more money for the freight charges."

A little smile started on Mr. Franco's face. "When I was a boy," he said, "we didn't pay money for things to play on. We made them."

"Do you think we could build things?" asked Maggie.

"I'll get my tools!" said Mr. Franco. "You could make things from old pipes and lumber from the dump. Ask everyone on Eighth Street to help."

"We'll have a playground made by hand!" yelled Maggie and Jay.

All the neighbors pitched in and worked hard to clean up the empty lot. On weekends they hammered and sawed and fastened together some monkey bars from little pipes. They got some very large pipes for the smaller kids to play in. And they made a slide and some swings from old lumber.

By the eighth week, the playground was finished. It was fun playing in the eight big pipes and in houses made from painted wooden boxes. There was a bike path, too.

When the work was over, Jay and Maggie gave a picnic for all the neighbors at the playground. And that day they named it the "Franco Good Luck Playground."

Photo by Doug Martin

whine

white

whimper

wheel

whether

wheat

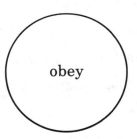

obey

site	heel	fine	rich
white	wheel	whine	which
while	whether	while	whimper

Care of a Puppy

Gail Bond got a little puppy as a gift from her uncle. In the box with the puppy was a book telling many things about the care of puppies.

1. You should try to make puppies feel at home. It may take a while until they feel settled. They may whine or whimper when they are left by themselves at night.

2. Puppies need several meals a day for a while. Dry puppy meal is best, but you may mix it with water. When they are older, dogs need just one meal a day. Dogs must always have fresh water to drink.

3. It is not good to let puppies have bones to play with or to eat. If the bones splinter, the puppy could easily choke.

4. Puppies must be kept clean. Try to brush them each day. The people who sell dogs can tell you when they should have baths. Use a soap that

is safe for dogs. Always dry your puppy well after a bath.

5. When dogs are older, they need shots. Ask an animal doctor, or "vet," when it's time for shots.

6. Training is important for all puppies. You must teach them to be clean in the house, but never strike them. You can be gentle and still train them to obey. When your puppy obeys say, "Good dog, good dog."

7. It's up to you whether you want your dog to bark at strangers, but dogs shouldn't bark at the family. Teach them not to run after things with wheels or to chase cats.

8. Puppies should not be teased. Play gently with your puppy. Don't try to anger it, even in fun.

9. When puppies have a collar and leash, they can be trained to "heel." This means they will stay close to you when they are taken somewhere. Next, puppies can be trained to sit still when they are told. Puppies make much better pets when they are well trained.

Never Shop With a Puppy

Gail Bond took one last look at her shopping list.

Notebook	1
Pencils	7
Schoolbag	1
Paperback books	3
Sneakers	1 pair
Socks	4 pairs

"Maybe I'd better make that five pairs of socks," she said as she changed the number. "There, that should do it!"

With her list finished, Gail had just one more thing to do. She had to get her mom to let her take her puppy, Harry, with them on the shopping trip.

"Please, Mom," she coaxed. "I'll do anything if you'll let him go." At last Mrs. Bond agreed that Harry could go. So Gail, her mom, and Harry started down the street.

Harry was a good puppy when Gail and her mom went into the card shop to get things for her schoolbag. He was even better when they got Gail's sneakers. Gail had to think whether she wanted red sneakers or white ones. It took a while for her to say she wanted the white ones. But Harry didn't seem to care about the wait. He just sat by her chair, wagging his tail.

When it was time to go, Harry happily followed Gail and her mom to the department store. There Gail got a white jacket and some socks. The clerk wrapped them neatly in a package. And that left Gail with a lot of things to carry—the puppy, the sneakers, the jacket, and her school things.

Gail turned to her mom. "Can't the store send my jacket home on a truck? I can't carry so many things!"

"I don't think the store will send a little package like that on a truck," said Mrs. Bond.

"But I can't carry so many things," Gail began to whine. "I'll drop something!"

"Well, I'll take one," said Mrs. Bond. "Which one do you want me to carry for you?"

"Please take Harry," said Gail.

"Oh, no," said Mrs. Bond. "Harry is your package. You take Harry. I'll take your jacket."

It was while they were on their way home that Harry became a problem. He must have told himself that it was time to play because by the time they reached the market, his paws had made marks all over Gail's packages. It didn't help that the store manager had written NO DOGS on a big, white card at the entrance. Gail and Harry had to wait by the entrance.

If Mrs. Bond hadn't taken so long in the store, things might not have gotten so bad. But she had to pick up a roast. And she had to look in different places for a box of rice, a can of green beans, and some wheat germ. Then she had a long visit with the store manager. When she went to pay for her things, she had to wait in a long line of people.

While Mrs. Bond was shopping, Harry began to wiggle and whimper. "Stop it, Harry!" said Gail. But Harry wouldn't obey. While Gail was trying to keep him still, her packages fell. When she reached for them, Harry got away. Then he quickly ran between the wheels of a parked car. It took three people to help Gail catch him.

When Mrs. Bond came back at last, Gail had piled her torn packages into a cart that belonged to the store. Harry was in the cart, too.

It seemed like a good way to handle the problem. But Mrs. Bond said, "We can't use the cart to take these things home. We'll have to get a taxicab. And all because of your puppy! I suppose I shouldn't have let you bring Harry with us. Next time, we'll leave him at home."

The next day, Mrs. Bond came home with a collar and leash for Harry. After that, Gail did not have such a hard time when she wanted to take Harry different places with her. But from then on, she never ever tried to take Harry shopping.

How To Write a Letter

	305 Maple Street
address	Dale, Wisconsin 58960
date	May 15, 1985
greeting	Dear Bob,

greeting   Dear Bob,

body   My dog had five puppies last week. I would like to share the puppies with my pals. Would you like to have one? They're all black with white spots. Tell your mom they're no problem at all. I've yet to hear them whine or whimper!

Please write and tell me. I could bring one to you on our next visit to Milton.

closing   Your pal,

Robert

third

dirt

first

walk

talk

chalk

sure

library

tall	bird	dirt	small
talk	third	first	wall
chalk	dirt	third	walk

A Good Library

One of the best places in Grove Street School was the library. Ms. Montez was in charge of the library. She liked to plan interesting things for the classes to see and do there.

One time she filled some shelves with puppets. Some of the puppets were made of wood. Others were like rag dolls. There were even some from Japan. Next to the puppets were library books about them. Many students made puppets for the first time after they saw those books. Puppets became the talk of the school!

Another time Ms. Montez set up three tables to show the shells she and her husband had collected on vacation trips. On the third table, she placed several books about seashells. Those books were enjoyed by nearly everyone in the school.

When spring came, Ms. Montez began to plan for her third show in the library. She said to herself, "This would be a good time of year to have a bird show. I'm sure it would make students more interested in the library books about birds."

Ms. Montez asked some students to help her with the show. Ted and Jan were very willing to help. They were sure they could think of ways to make the show a good one.

Ted said his family had some books about birds. He offered to bring them to the library. He also planned a talk on birds.

Jan liked to draw in chalk. She showed Ms. Montez some chalk drawings she had made of birds. She offered to hang them in the halls near the library.

Ms. Montez had several very good tapes of the different calls birds make. She was sure the classes would like them. She hoped some of the students might even make tapes themselves.

Then Mr. Kelly said he could get some stuffed birds from a man who collected them. He also offered to fix a place for these birds using dirt, grass, and branches. The stuffed birds would look quite real in such a setting.

Best of all, Ms. Montez and her husband

promised to take some of the students on a walk along the dirt paths near the school. Before the walk, the boys and girls were to read about the birds that nested in or near Grove City. Then on Saturday they would look for all these birds. They would try to name the birds they saw.

The whole school became interested in the bird show in the library. Lots of students, even the first-graders, lent books from home. One student said he would show slides of birds, and the music teacher wrote a song just for the show.

Ms. Montez was quite pleased with the plans for the bird show. But she was even happier on the first day of the show. Mr. Kelly's class had a big surprise for her. Fred spoke for the rest of the class. He said, "Ms. Montez, all of us in this room have a gift for you. It was made just for you by a man who carves birds from wood and paints them. From now on you can always have at least one bird in the library."

From that day on a bright red cardinal sat on a branch on the main desk of the Grove Street School library.

Illustration by Marie DeJohn

The Card Catalog

The next time you go to a library, look for the card catalog. You can save time by using the card catalog when you need to look for a book. It is much faster to use the catalog than it is to look on all the library shelves.

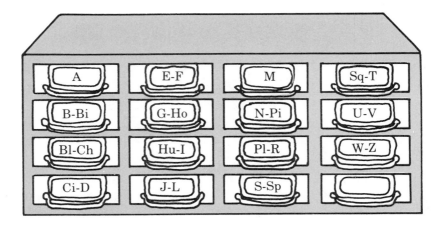

In which drawer would you look for these books and topics?

dogs	Indians	*Yesterday and Today*
birds	volleyball	*Kittens for Kelley*
puppets	*Cry of the Hawk*	*Hundreds of Hats*
water	*Harry at Home*	*Strange Visitors*

knot

knit

knock

knuckle

knapsack

knee

know

knew

scout

out

shout

spout

tree knee know	shot shout scout	not knot knit	spot spout out

At the Scout Camp

Jan, Dan, and Pam were all scouts. Jan was a Girl Scout. Dan was a Boy Scout. And Pam was a Brownie Scout. Pam knew that Jan and Dan enjoyed scout camp. She could hardly wait until she could become a Girl Scout. Then she could go to camp, too.

The scout camp that Jan and Dan went to was about twenty miles from their home. Mr. Bell knew Pam wanted to see the camp. So at ten o'clock one Saturday morning, he went to see Pam's dad.

"Good morning, Gus," said Mr. Bell. "Dot and I are going to visit Dan at scout camp today. We have room in the car for you and Pam if you'd like to go along."

"Thanks, Tom," said Mr. Sands, "but I have so much to do. I was in the basement painting the kitchen chairs when you knocked."

"That's a shame," said Mr. Bell. "It's such a nice day. Would Pam like to go with us?"

Pam really wanted to see the scout camp, so she ran to her room and dressed in her Brownie outfit. She ran back into the kitchen carrying her sneakers. "Dad, can you help me get the knots out of these laces?" she asked. "Please hurry."

"Take your time," said Mr. Bell. "I'll wait." Pam and her dad worked on the knots. When the laces were unknotted, Pam slipped the sneakers on. She kissed her dad good-by and went off with Mr. Bell.

In the car Pam kept thinking of things she wanted to ask the scouts about camping. But when they got to the camp, the scout leader explained that visiting time did not begin until after lunch.

Dan smiled and waved to them from his tent. "Glad to see you, Pam!" he shouted. But he had to help out with the camp cleanup. So he went right on working.

Later, Pam ate a picnic lunch with Mr. and Mrs. Bell. It was good, but the hamburgers the scouts were frying smelled much better. It didn't help when Pam spilled ketchup all over the knit shirt

Mr. Bell wore. She was quickly becoming very unhappy.

Visiting time came at last, but Dan raced right past. "I'll be right back," he called out. "Brad cut his knee, and we need the knapsack with the first-aid kit for him."

Mr. Bell yelled, "Be careful!" Then he added, "I hope he comes right back."

Pam was thinking, "I hope so, too. Visiting time will be over in a little while."

After a while they saw Dan in his swim trunks. He waved to them and shouted, "Do you want to see me take my swimming test?"

Pam sat with Mr. and Mrs. Bell on a big rock. Dan dived, and the water spouted up. By the time he had passed his test and changed into dry things, it was five o'clock.

"Maybe Dan will be able to sit with us for a while before supper," said Mrs. Bell. But Dan had to spend the time before supper looking for firewood and building a campfire.

Then Pam and Mr. and Mrs. Bell had to get back. Pam had hardly talked to Dan. She didn't know one thing she hadn't known before.

A week later, Mr. Bell saw Pam. "Do you want to ride to the scout camp? We have to pick up Dan."

Pam knew there was no reason to get into her Brownie outfit this time. So she just dressed in a shorts set her grandmother had knitted for her. Then she ran out and jumped into the car.

On the ride home, Dan sat in the back with Pam. At last she got to hear all about the things that happen at scout camp. She asked so many things that Dan didn't stop talking until they got to Grove Street.

When the car stopped in front of Pam's house, Dan said, "Wait a second." Then he took his scout knife out of his pocket and said, "Here, Scout, you'll be needing this."

Scouting

Have you ever seen scouts starting out on a camping trip? They carry much of their camping gear in knapsacks on their backs. Each of them may have a cup, a dish, a knife, a fork, and blankets.

Scouts must know good safety habits before they go on a camping trip. They are trained to work and play in ways that are safe. However, sometimes things can go wrong. That's why scouts also carry first-aid kits on their hikes or camping trips. Each scout must know how to treat a scraped knee or skinned knuckles. Scouts must be able to bandage a sprained ankle or wrist.

The scouts are now set to do their work and have fun. They will pitch tents and collect firewood to build fires for cooking. They will also raise the scout flag. For many of these jobs they will need to know how to make different knots in ropes. A scout who has passed the knot-making test knows at least ten different knots.

When all the work is finished, the scouts may go swimming or take a hike. The hard work and fresh air make the scouts very hungry, so the meals they cook over the campfire are quickly eaten. After they have eaten, the scouts pitch in and clean up. Then they sit near the campfire and sing songs about scouting. After the last song, everyone knows it is time for a good night's sleep. A hard but happy day in the woods has ended.

Photo Courtesy of Boy Scouts of America

Forms and More Forms!

There are so many different forms for so many different things! There are job forms, school forms, and order forms. One day you may have to fill out a form like this:

☐ Send me the FREE book about cars.

☑ Send me the FREE book about travel.

PLEASE PRINT:

NAME   _JONES_   _JEAN_
               (Last)   (First)

ADDRESS   _574 SUNSET DRIVE_

CITY _DUBLIN_   STATE _OHIO_   ZIP _43208_

loud
cloud

sound
round
around
ground

through

land	pond	round	loud
loud	pound	around	cloud
cloud	round	ground	

Thunder and Lightning

George T. Ladd and John F. Savage

Have you ever seen a thunderstorm? What happens? You see round clouds get big and dark. Then you see a bright flash of lightning and hear the loud pounding sound of thunder. After that the rain starts and the wind gets strong and cool.

What makes thunder and lightning?

Before a thunderstorm, the air near the ground is hot and damp. This air rises. As the air rises, it

Photo Courtesy of National Center for Atmospheric Research (NCAR)

gets cooler. This cooler air forms small water drops. The water drops then form clouds.

As the air keeps rising, more and more drops are made. This makes the clouds get thick and dark. It also makes them grow taller. At last a cloud stops getting taller. It begins to round out at the top. It forms a thundercloud.

The small water drops shift around in the cloud and make bits of electricity. More and more water drops rub together to make more and more electricity. Then the electricity flashes. We call this flash lightning.

The lightning travels from the cloud to the ground. It also jumps from one cloud to another.

After each flash of lightning comes thunder. When lightning flashes, it heats the air around it very fast. It drives the air away. When this air gets back to where it was before, it makes a loud sound. This loud crash is the sound of thunder.

We don't hear thunder until we have seen lightning. Light travels through the air much faster than sound, just as a jet plane can fly faster than a bird. This is why we see lightning before we hear thunder.

Because light travels faster than sound, we can judge how close the lightning is. Look at the lightning and listen for the thunder. Count the seconds between the lightning flash and the sound of the thunder. If the storm is far away, there will be a long time between the lightning and the thunder. If the thunder sounds come right after the lightning, we know the lightning is close.

Sometimes we can see lightning, but we can't hear any thunder. Some people call this lightning "heat lightning." We do not hear the thunder because the storm is too far away for the sound to reach us.

Thunderstorms can be harmful. Thunder is not harmful, but wind and lightning can be. The wind can blow down trees onto houses and wires. When lightning hits the land, it can knock poles and trees to the ground. It can start fires and harm people and animals. But there is no need to be afraid of lightning if you know what to do.

Do NOT stay outside in a thunderstorm. Try to get inside a house or a car. You can watch the storm through the window of your house, but do not stand too close to the window. Don't make any calls. You should stay away from all metal things around your home as well as the sink and the bathtub. Why? The electricity from the lightning may be drawn to the metal in wires and pipes. Then it can travel through the metal to you.

If you can't get inside a house or a car, do not stand under a tree or in an open place. Lightning may hit the tallest thing around, so stay low until you can get to a safe shelter.

After a while the rain will get lighter, the wind will slow down, and the thunder and lightning will stop. The dark clouds will begin to drift away. The storm will be over.

hour

couch

ouch

bounce

ounce

move

heard

shout	ouch	out	bounce
couch	ounce	our	ounce
ouch	bounce	hour	ouch

Who's There?

Mr. and Mrs. Benton had worked very hard lately. Mrs. Benton had spent long hours at her shop. She even had to hire three more clerks to help with the work. Mr. Benton had worked long hours on his job as well. He was starting to think about looking for a different one.

One day he said to his wife, "Sally, why don't we take a little vacation? We need to get away."

"You're right, Mark," said Sally. "Let's rent a cabin by the lake, just for a day or so. We could ask your mom and dad to stay with Jim and Kim. That way they won't have to miss school."

So the next week Grandpa and Grandma Benton came to stay with Jim and Kim. Grandpa Benton was lots of fun. He always had a story to tell. But it was Grandma who began to tell scary stories on Sunday night.

As they sat together on the couch, she told one story after another. Each story seemed to be better than the one before. Jim and Kim could have listened for hours, but Grandma said, "You have to get up for school in the morning. You should be in bed right now."

Jim and Kim went to their rooms and slid way down under the blankets. But Jim couldn't get to sleep. He tossed and turned for what seemed like hours.

Suddenly he sat up in bed! "What was that?" he said to himself. "I know I heard something move." He sat very still, waiting to hear it, but everything was silent. He wiggled down under the blankets and lay still. "It was just the wind," he told himself. "If I had an ounce of sense, I'd turn over and go to sleep."

Just then someone bumped into something in the dark. "Ouch!"

"Who's there?" asked Jim. "What do you want?"

"It's Kim," said his sister as she came into the room. "I think I heard a scratching sound outside. Did you?"

"I heard something," said Jim bravely. "But it was just a tree or something blowing across the window. Now go back to sleep."

Just then they both heard the scratching sound. Kim knew from the look on Jim's face that he was as scared as she was. "We've got to go downstairs and look around," said Kim. "What if someone has broken in?"

"Well, we can't do anything about it now!" said Jim.

"Come on," said Kim. "We've got to see who's out there or call for help."

"OK, but be careful, and don't make a sound," said Jim.

As they stepped into the hallway, they stayed very close together. Slowly they crept down the stairs, one by one. Then they quickly slipped past the couch in the front room. As they stepped into the kitchen, something jumped at Jim and nearly knocked him down. He gasped with fright as Kim reached for the light switch.

There stood Kim's dog, Sandy, wagging his tail. He was so happy to see them he bounced around the room. Then he sat down and waited for a pat. "Oh, no!" Kim and Jim said together.

"That scary sound was just Sandy trying to get out of the kitchen!" said Kim.

"Grandma's scary stories really worked on us!" said Jim.

Good-by, Grove Street!

One day Mr. Benton found a job he liked much better than his old one. But it was in Riverside, a town about twenty-five miles away. The road to Riverside had a lot of traffic and a lot of traffic lights. So it took Mr. Benton an hour longer to get to work. And it took him an hour longer to get home.

One night the traffic was very bad. Mr. Benton didn't reach home until eight o'clock. Mrs. Benton, Jim, and Kim had all eaten at six. Mr. Benton had to eat alone.

"This is too hard for us," said his wife. "You are out of the house before Jim, Kim, and I get up in the morning. You get home so late we can't even have dinner with you."

"Yes, and that means I can't do much around here these days," said Mr. Benton. "I miss doing things with you and the children."

"I have a plan," said Mrs. Benton. "Let's look

for a house close to your work. That way you won't have as long a drive. And we'd be closer to my mother's apartment in Riverside."

"I don't know," said Mr. Benton. "We like it here. We like the people, and the children are very happy. Let me think about it."

The next day Mr. Benton said that his wife's plan sounded good. That weekend they looked for a house near Riverside. They looked until they found a house that was the right size and price and was near a good school.

"Look!" Jim shouted as they were looking at the house. "There are boys and girls playing in the next yard!"

The people who were selling the house said, "It's an older home. And it has lots of room for your family. A little paper and some outside paint are all it needs."

"Well, I'll have time to paint the outside of the house in the spring," said Mr. Benton. "We can get the paper on the walls right away."

While the house near Riverside was being fixed up, Grandma Lang, Mrs. Benton's mother, came to the old house in Grove City. She helped with the packing. She spent hours packing away lamps, dishes, and glasses.

Then she found many things that didn't fit Jim and Kim any longer. She made a pile of them for smaller children in a family she knew.

At last the day of the move came. The van stopped in front of the Bentons' house. All the people on Grove Street came to say good-by. Pam's father asked, "When will you be back to visit us?"

"It won't be long," said Mr. Benton. "And we want you to visit us, too."

By the time they had all said good-by, the movers had finished packing things in the van. One of the movers held the fish tank on her lap so the fish wouldn't bounce out along the way.

Mrs. Lang and all the Bentons got into the family car. As they drove off, Jim and Kim waved and shouted, "Good-by, Grove Street, good-by, good-by!"

Have You Seen These?

Photos by Doug Martin

1. If you're looking for a camping spot, look for this.

2. This means something isn't safe. Be very careful!

3. This tells you to stay out!

4. This tells you that you're coming to a railroad crossing.

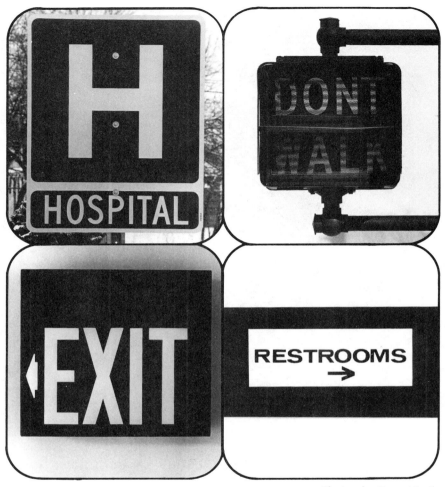

Photos by Doug Martin

5. This tells you where the restrooms are.

6. Look for this if you want to leave a building.

7. This tells you where the hospital is.

8. This tells when you can cross the street.

relax
recall
repay
report

(been)   (principal)

tall
call
recall

say
pay
repay

lap
tax
relax

sort
port
report

Clean Up! Fix Up!

The students in the upper grades at Grove Street School were very excited. They had been told that the mayor of Grove City was coming to their school. She was going to ask them to help the city.

Randy, who was in Ted's class, said, "I bet she's going to ask us to collect money for the city. I recall someone saying that the city needs more money for parks and playgrounds."

"I don't think so," said Ted. "The mayor wouldn't ask us just to collect money. I'll bet she has a project for us."

On the big day all the students were asked to report to the assembly room. The mayor and the principal of the school walked onto the stage. The students sang their school song. Then the mayor got up to speak.

"Boys and girls of Grove Street School," she said, "I am very glad to be able to speak to you today. The city needs your help in cleaning and fixing up the neighborhood around your building. This neighborhood is in much better shape than it was years ago. But we can't relax. If we do, our streets and homes will go downhill. Will you help us?"

After the mayor had finished talking, the students began to clap. Then the principal said the school would be glad to help with the mayor's plan. She said it would be a good way to repay the people of the neighborhood for their help with the school.

Each class was to clean and fix up one block on a street near the school. The people in the houses on that street had been asked to help, too. A report would be made to the principal every week.

The girls and boys in Mr. Silver's fifth grade class met to plan their work. Becky said, "I think we should ask the people on our block to paint their houses if they need to. My father says that's the best thing to do."

"You would have to be careful about that," said Mr.

Silver. "Maybe you could just hint that fresh paint would look nice or offer to help with small jobs."

Then a boy in the class said, "I'd like to ask people to use plastic trash bags. Sometimes paper bags fall apart before they're collected. Then the trash is left on the street."

"That's good," said one girl. "And we could offer to help some older people carry out their trash. It's hard for them to get up and down steps sometimes."

At last one student said, "Mr. Silver, I want to help make the street look nicer. Could we get some flowers? We could plant them in boxes or in the yards."

"I recall that the man in the plant shop on the corner said he wanted to help. You could ask him about the flowers," said Mr. Silver.

The next week the students in Grove Street School went to work. The people in the neighborhood were glad to help. Many of the children worked on the block where their homes were. The fathers and mothers of these children seemed to work extra hard!

The best day of all was the day TV reporters came to see the work that was going on. That night some of the students were thrilled to see themselves on TV.

At the end of the first week, there was another assembly. Each class gave a report on its work. The principal and the teachers were very pleased.

After the reports the principal said, "You have been doing a very fine job this first week. But we mustn't relax. Let's keep up the good work. Then we can really be proud of our neighborhood."

The students of Grove Street School kept working on their project. They were proud indeed when the mayor returned to their school. First she thanked them for all their good work. Then to repay them for their help, she gave the principal a state flag to be hung in the main hall. Along with the flag was a card that said:

> Grove City thanks the students
> of Grove Street School for making
> their city a better place.

TO THE TEACHER

The MERRILL LINGUISTIC READING PROGRAM consists of eight Readers developed on linguistic principles applicable to the teaching of reading. The rationale of the program and detailed teaching procedures are described in the Teacher's Edition of each Reader.

All words introduced in this Reader are listed on the following pages under the headings "Words in Pattern," "Sight Words," and "Applications of Patterning."

Words listed as "Words in Pattern" include matrixes in the third major set of spelling patterns (those containing the vowel combination *oa*) and a number of minor sets of spelling patterns.

Words listed as "Sight Words" are high-frequency words introduced to provide normal sentence patterns in the stories.

Words listed as "Applications of Patterning" include new words based on patterns and sight words previously introduced, combinations of words (compound words), additional tense forms, plurals, possessives, and contractions.

WORD LISTS FOR TEACHER REFERENCE

Pages	Words in Pattern	Sight Words
Unit 1 5-12	might sight night tight flight bright	people because
Unit 2 13-18	road toad load loaf soap soak croak	
Unit 3 19-28	coat boat goat float roast boast	even
Unit 4 29-36	cent center cell cedar city circle	table work while
Unit 5 37-44	nice rice price ice face Grace place space spruce	bacteria laugh

Pages	Words in Pattern	Sight Words
Unit 6 45-52	tackle ankle tinkle jingle juggle chuckle tumble ruffle	circus town
Unit 7 53-62	beetle steeple bugle title idle maple	giant
Unit 8 63-68	ledge edge dodge judge budge ridge bridge	build
Unit 9 69-76	rage wage age engage range change strange	pound baby monkey

Pages	Words in Pattern	Sight Words
Unit 10 77-82	cabbage luggage package damage image beverage manage	vacation aunt
Unit 11 83-90	bulge danger stranger passenger	carry future
Unit 12 91-98	gentle germ German geranium ginger giraffe	any many
Unit 13 99-104	wrap wrist wreck wrench write wrote wrong saw raw	
Unit 14 105-110	weigh neighbor weight freight eight eighth	
Unit 15 111-118	whine white whimper wheel whether wheat	obey

Pages	Words in Pattern	Sight Words
Unit 16 119-124	third dirt first walk talk chalk	sure library
Unit 17 125-132	knot knit knock knuckle knapsack knee know knew scout out shout spout	
Unit 18 133-138	loud cloud sound round around ground	through
Unit 19 139-148	hour couch ouch bounce ounce	move heard
Unit 20 149-153	relax recall repay report	been principal

Unit 1 <u>5-12</u>	Unit 1 <u>5-12</u> cont.	Unit 2 <u>13-18</u> cont.	Unit 3 <u>19-28</u> cont.	Unit 3 <u>19-28</u> cont.
agreed	right	keeps	comets	secretly
air	restful	lakes	crater	secrets
also	rocket	lays	crept	settled
balls	rockets	loads	crossing	shore
battles	satellites	mass	deeper	silent
became	share	middle	Dipper	skimmed
between	shedding	polliwogs	docked	sleepy
blast	shone	problems	dreams	slick
blasting	signals	remember	eaten	sometime
chair	site	roads	fairy	sore
Chinese	speaking	several	falling	speaker
classmates	squeezed	shiny	fear	spotted
darkness	steered	shorter	floated	stories
displays	study	simple	floating	surprise
dreamed	suppose	soaked	followed	Texas
easy	tightly	somehow	forest	thud
equipment	travels	startle	front	tired
exciting	trees	sunlight	giggled	treetops
fasten	twenty	sunshine	gloomy	wide
flame	years	swellings	goblins	wishes
flashing		tadpole	grassy	within
flights	**Unit 2**	tadpoles	hilltops	woke
forth	<u>13-18</u>	toads	hoped	
garden		tonight	hopes	**Unit 4**
happens	alike	tried	hungry	<u>29-36</u>
hardly	appear	watch	Kelly's	
Ibon	become	ways	kings	apartment
interested	body	wiggles	lost	apple
invented	brag	year	luckily	apples
land	careful		makes	backyard
leader	changes		Milky	banana
leaders	chase	**Unit 3**	Milly	baseball
lean	chased	<u>19-28</u>	moment	basketball
light	clean		monsters	baskets
lights	croaked	anger	munching	both
longed	daytime	ashore	nowhere	brother
Mars	differ	barely	paper	candlestick
members	disappears	Beachwood	park	candlesticks
mighty	dull	blazing	peak	cells
model	dusty	blocked	peanuts	cents
orbit	expect	bobbed	pleased	checkers
over	facts	branches	queens	chess
perfect	female	brightly	rail	Chestnut
planet	fishlike	carnival	rise	chose
planets	flatter	chairs	riverboat	circles
players	flying	choked	roasted	copper
power	gardens	clear	rocked	craft
powerful	harmful	clearing	sailed	crafts
probably	hides	closer	sailing	dishes
project	I'd	coats	scary	dresses
provide	jellylike	collecting	scream	ending

Unit 1 29-36 cont.	Unit 5 37-44	Unit 5 37-44 cont.	Unit 6 45-52 cont.	Unit 7 53-62 cont.
exit	beans	yells	spinning	reason
families	buttermilk	yesterday	stumbled	sharp
family's	cartons		supposed	shy
fifty	cashed	**Unit 6**	tackled	smelled
frozen	cattle	**45-52**	teeny	smiling
grandparents	chart		tinkled	snapped
grapes	charts	act	trained	sneaking
greens	chatted	acts	trainer	stammered
hamburgers	checker	ankles	tramp	staring
hams	cheese	balanced	tripped	stomped
jail	chilled	bareback	turn	stream
jars	churn	barked	turning	they've
Jean	collects	barking	umbrella	thinks
kitchens	cool	begun	Uncle	titles
Ling	cornflakes	brown	waited	trespassing
lonely	crabmeat	chuckled		vines
market	cream	clanging	**Unit 7**	weekends
member	dairy	clown	**53-62**	welcome
miles	dairy's	clowns		who's
mixes	explain	clown's	able	woman's
Oak	fade	clowns'	Ash	
parks	farmers	coal	ashamed	**Unit 8**
peeked	flattened	crowd	ashes	**63-68**
pitcher	freezer	danced	cave	
pretzels	frown	dizzy	caves	arms
prizes	heated	down	Crane	aside
public	hoses	exits	Crane's	beams
rocking	kills	faces	Crossbend	blamed
rope	laughed	fighter	Dave	bridges
seed	lemons	fire	Dave's	brooks
shaped	listen	flippers	Emma	brush
shelves	marketing	forty	fallen	builders
sizes	milked	harness	fireplaces	building
snapshot	mine	harnesses	fires	built
sorts	mopping	heels	gossip	bumpy
spokes	notebook	horses'	grapevine	cod
stacks	peas	jingled	grapevines	concrete
staying	places	juggled	groaned	connect
stone	popcorn	lemonade	heaped	cracks
store	popping	lively	leaves	day's
streets	prices	Nineteenth	Man's	fairly
stretch	printed	paying	mean	helmet
supermarket	says	please	names	hurt
swung	skim	plopped	napkin	jungles
tables	smells	poles	needles	ledges
visitors	stops	ruffles	Peter	likely
volleyball	takes	Russ	placed	market
windows	trucks	Russ's	plate	painters
wore	unpack	saddles	plucked	painting
working	veal	seal	pretending	perhaps
	Winters	sights	rather	

Applications of Patterning
(The underlined numbers are page numbers.)

Unit 8 63-68 cont.	Unit 9 69-76 cont.	Unit 10 77-82 cont.	Unit 11 83-90 cont.	Unit 12 91-98 cont.
raised	jungle	iced	piles	swaying
remembered	keeper	joked	presses	tulips
risks	keepers	Kerny	prevent	vivid
riverbanks	keeper's	lamb	prisoners	weeds
rivers	lettuce	lining	rack	yanked
roadway	male	manager	raising	
ropes	misses	sniffing	roadside	**Unit 13**
safer	monkeys		scanner	**99-104**
sledgehammer	nests		seams	
smashed	nilly	**Unit 11**	smelly	ad
steel	orangutan	**83-90**	somewhere	anything
steeples	orangutans		Speedy	ax
streams	pages	agree	Spiff	brushes
swinging	pounds	alarmed	Spike	chisel
timber	puffy	becoming	Spinner	crops
towns	raced	breathe	states	downtown
train	scales	bulged	survive	dwellers
trains	shaggy	button	tossed	enclosed
wider	skate	carrying	tossing	fighting
worked	skating	closes	urgent	garment
workers	smarter	crushers	U.S.A.	hole
	stamp	dangers		holes
Unit 9	tales	evening	**Unit 12**	homework
69-76	tamed	Everytown	**91-98**	Lee
	teaching	everywhere		Lees
apart	toss	excuse	carried	lumber
baby's	travel	file	daffodils	lumberyard
Bamboo	treetop	filth	drab	mailed
bars	ugly	filthy	dreamily	metals
belong	upright	fines	easily	needle
cage	upside	gang	edges	ourselves
cages	wages	garbage	flower	planting
chattering	willy	grime	gentleman	printing
cheeks	wishing	habit	gently	rap
chimp	zoos	hate	geraniums	seventh
chimpanzee		huge	Germany	scraping
chimpanzees		important	germs	shape
chimps	**Unit 10**	invaded	giraffes	sharpened
dare	**77-82**	lazy	golden	skinning
ducked		leave	gowns	spears
engaged	baggage	litter	nicer	sprained
fact	barnyard	litterbags	pansies	tool
feelings	carefully	lives	perk	toolmaking
fists	Carl	march	playfully	tools
gibbon	Carl's	message	raked	wrenches
gibbons	cried	moaning	seeds	writing
gorilla	damaged	nab	seems	
gorillas	exchange	otherwise	selected	**Unit 14**
Grover	farmhouse	papers	sneeze	**105-110**
Hines	grazing	passengers	spice	charges
jeep	happily	perform	spring	costs

Unit 14 105-110 cont.	Unit 15 111-118 cont.	Unit 17 125-132	Unit 17 125-132 cont.	Unit 19 139-148 cont.
Franco	strangers	aid	unknotted	hallway
Franco's	strike	bandage		hire
gatekeeper	taxicab	basement	**Unit 18**	hours
hammered	teased	blankets	**133-138**	lamps
Jay	training	Brad	blow	Lang
Jay's	"vet"	Brownie	clouds	listened
large	wheels	campfire	cooler	movers
Maggie	Wisconsin	cleanup	count	restrooms
meaning	wrapped	dived	damp	Riverside
neighbors	written	Dublin	drawn	rooms
playground		explained	drift	scratching
railroad		firewood	drives	sense
sales		fork	electricity	slowly
sawed	**Unit 16**	form	flashes	sounded
tracks	**119-124**	forms	fly	switch
washes		frying	grow	traffic
	calls	gear	harm	weekend
	cardinal	habits	heat	we've
Unit 15	carves	hikes	heats	wife's
111-118	catalog	however	lighter	
changed	charge	hurry	lightning	
choke	draw	kits	low	**Unit 20**
clerk	drawer	knapsacks	outside	**149-153**
closing	drawings	knife	pounding	assembly
coaxed	graders	knitted	rises	Becky
collar	halls	knocked	rising	cleaning
Dale	happier	knots	shelter	corner
department	hawk	known	shift	downhill
entrance	Indians	knows	slow	excited
hadn't	Japan	knuckles	sounds	extra
Harry	Kelley	laces	starts	grades
leash	Montez	needing	storm	mayor
marks	music	night's	tallest	mayor's
means	nested	o'clock	thunder	neighborhood
Milton	offered	Ohio	thundercloud	playgrounds
neatly	paints	outfit	thunderstorm	port
obeys	promised	print	thunderstorms	proud
older	puppets	raise	wires	Randy
packages	Saturday	scouting		reporters
pairs	seashells	scouts	**Unit 19**	reports
paperback	setting	scraped	**139-148**	returned
paws	show	shirt		Silver
pencils	showed	shouted	blowing	Silver's
puppies	slides	skinned	bounced	stage
rich	student	spouted	bravely	tax
Robert	students	starting	clerks	teachers
schoolbag	stuffed	talked	downstairs	thrilled
shots	tapes	talking	found	upper
sneakers	topics	tents	fright	walked
splinter	whole	trunks	gasped	yards

1 2 3 4 5 6 7 8 9 10 11 12 13 14 15 — 92 91 90 89 88 87 86 85

Editorial and Production Staff

Project Editor, Connie S. Johnson; *Editor,* Susan Weber; *Designer,* Scott D. Sommers; *Project Artist,* Michael T. Henry; *Photo Editor,* Barbara Buchholz; *Production Editor,* Joy E. Dickerson